Usborne English Re

Level 2

Robin Hood
and the
Silver Arrow

Retold by Mairi Mackinnon

Illustrated by Rose Frith

English language consultant: Peter Viney

Contents

You can listen to the story online here:
www.usborneenglishreaders.com/
robinhoodandthesilverarrow

"Robbed, again!" The Sheriff of Nottingham looked angrily at his men. "There were six of you. You had fast horses, and good swords. You're some of my best soldiers – or that's what I thought."

"What could we do?" asked the captain. "Robin Hood's men surprised us when we were riding through Sherwood Forest. They came out of nowhere, fifteen or twenty of them. They all had bows and arrows. We didn't even have time to use our swords."

"That's the fourth time this year," said the Sheriff. "Robin Hood is laughing at me. He knows that he can hide anywhere in that forest. He knows that the people will protect him, even if I burn their farms and their villages. Nobody respects me, and nobody respects the law. I have to stop him."

"My men can't fight him in the forest," he thought. "Robin must come here, to Nottingham – but how can I persuade him to do that?"

A boy was walking slowly through the forest. He looked around, but all he could see was trees in every direction.

"Robin Hood?" he called. "Are you there?"

Suddenly there were men all around him. They were wearing green clothes and carrying bows and arrows. One of them stepped forward. "What can Robin Hood do for you?"

"I – we wanted to thank you. Things have been difficult in our village. We've had a bad winter, and the Sheriff takes everything he can from us. With the money that you give us, we can buy enough food until the spring."

"I'm glad to hear it," said Robin. "So tell me, what is the Sheriff doing now?"

"He's busy," said the boy. "He's having an archery contest, at Nottingham Castle. The prize for the best archer is a silver arrow."

"A silver arrow," said Robin. "I'd like to see that. I'd like to bring it back here to Sherwood."

"Robin, you can't go!" said a tall man. His name was John Little, but everyone called him Little John. "Don't you see? It's a trick!"

"Oh, but I think I can," said Robin. "I'm sure the Sheriff is expecting me, but he's never actually seen me, has he?"

"The Sheriff is telling everyone that Robin Hood won't come to the contest," said the boy. "He says that even Robin Hood isn't brave enough, or stupid enough."

"Well then, I think the Sheriff needs another surprise," said Robin.

The day of the contest was bright
and sunny. Hundreds of people came
to Nottingham Castle from the town and the
country all around. Some of the archers were
from Nottingham, but others came from
Chester or York or other towns, far away.

The contest was in a wide field next to
the castle. Around the edges of the field,
people were selling food and drink. Some
people were playing music, and others
were dancing. One man was walking on his
hands. Everyone was enjoying themselves.

The Sheriff was riding around the field on a black horse, and his lady was on a white horse beside him. The Sheriff could see a few men wearing green, but they were just ordinary townspeople and farmers with their families.

He looked at the archers. Some of them were his own soldiers, and he recognized a few more Nottingham men. His marshal was organizing the contest and talking to the archers, and the Sheriff rode over to them.

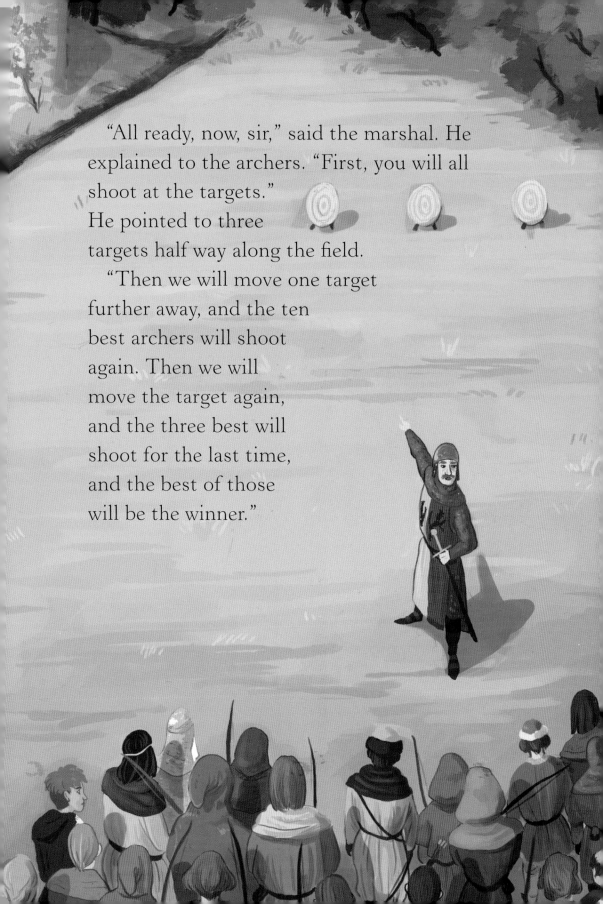

"All ready, now, sir," said the marshal. He explained to the archers. "First, you will all shoot at the targets." He pointed to three targets half way along the field.

"Then we will move one target further away, and the ten best archers will shoot again. Then we will move the target again, and the three best will shoot for the last time, and the best of those will be the winner."

The Sheriff got down from his horse to meet the archers. He looked at them closely. Robin Hood had fair hair and a beard, he knew. Here was a man with fair hair – but he was one of the Sheriff's own soldiers. Here was another – but he came from Chester, not Nottingham.

The Sheriff stopped in front of a man wearing old red clothes. He had dark hair and a sunburned face.

"Who are you?" the Sheriff asked.

"My name is Robert of Huntingdon," said the man. "I have been away from England for a few years. I was fighting in the wars, and I have learned to use a bow and arrow, you'll see."

"Hmm," said the Sheriff. "Robin Hood isn't here, anyway. I suppose he wasn't brave enough to leave Sherwood Forest."

The Sheriff and his lady sat down to watch the contest. Soldiers stood all around them to protect them. Then, one after another, the archers shot at the targets. Some of the arrows didn't hit the targets at all, and the crowd laughed. Some arrows hit the edges, and some were closer to the middle. A few were right in the middle of the target.

The marshal called the names of the ten best archers. The Sheriff's men moved one of the targets further away. One by one, the archers stepped forward and shot again. This time, only three arrows hit the middle of the target.

Three men waited for the Sheriff's men to move the target. One was the Sheriff's captain, one was the man from Chester and one was the man in red. The crowd was quiet, now. Everyone was watching.

The man from Chester shot his arrow.
It was very near the middle of the target,
and the crowd cheered loudly.

The captain shot next. This time, the
arrow was exactly in the middle but there
was no cheering from the crowd.

"You can't do better than that," the marshal said to the man in red, but the stranger wasn't listening. His arrow flew towards the target, hit the captain's arrow and split it in two. The crowd cheered even more loudly than before, and he went to take his prize.

"That's the best shooting I've ever seen," said the Sheriff. "You should come and work for me. I'll pay you well."

"I don't work for any man," said the stranger. "I have everything that I need."

The marshal looked angry, but the Sheriff smiled. "Take your prize, stranger. You're the best archer in the north of England, and I respect that. You're a better archer even than Robin Hood. Perhaps he knew, and that's why he stayed away from the contest."

"Long live Robin Hood!" shouted a man in the crowd. Suddenly the Sheriff's soldiers were everywhere. The people in the crowd were frightened, and everyone started running in different directions. Nobody saw the man in red again.

Later in Sherwood Forest, Robin Hood was washing the brown from his face and hair with river water.

"You're still brown, Robert of Huntingdon," laughed Little John. "You're going to be brown for a long time. Perhaps you can go back and persuade the Sheriff to give you that job."

Robin Hood laughed, too. "It was a good day. I'm only sorry about one thing. No, two things."

"What are they?"

"First, the Sheriff doesn't believe that Robin Hood was brave enough to come to the contest. Second, he thinks that there's a better archer than me."

"You should tell him the truth,"
said Little John. "Send him a message."
"And how can I do that? Who can I ask
to carry a message to Nottingham Castle,
when it's full of the Sheriff's soldiers?"
"I'll tell you," said Little John.

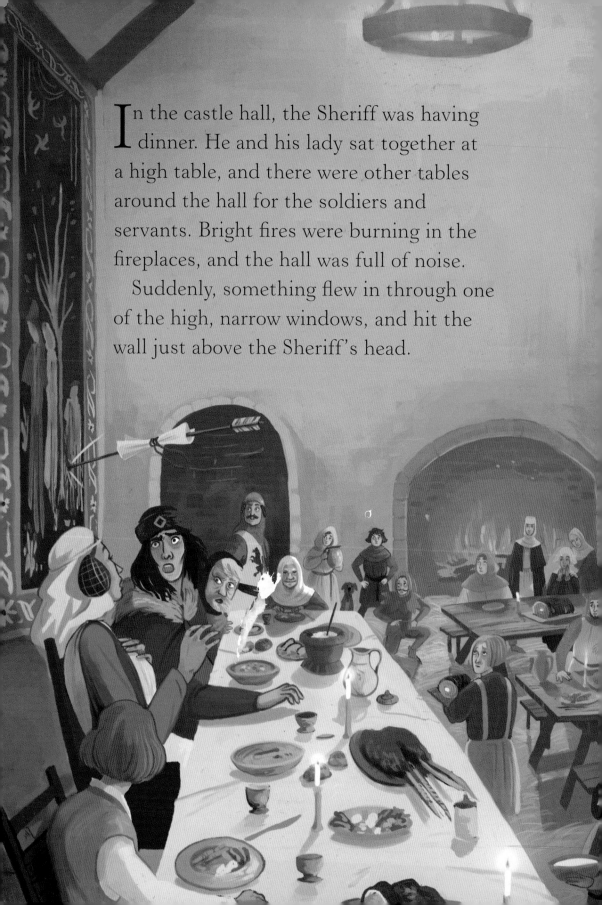

In the castle hall, the Sheriff was having dinner. He and his lady sat together at a high table, and there were other tables around the hall for the soldiers and servants. Bright fires were burning in the fireplaces, and the hall was full of noise.

Suddenly, something flew in through one of the high, narrow windows, and hit the wall just above the Sheriff's head.

"An arrow!" said the marshal. "What is this?"

"There's a piece of paper around it," said one of the servants. He gave the message to the Sheriff.

The Sheriff's face went white with anger as he read:

Our sheriff is a foolish man
Say all here in Sherwood.
Look who has won the silver prize –
Our hero, Robin Hood!

About Robin Hood

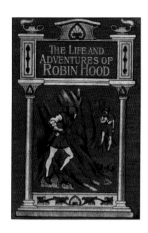

People have told stories and sung songs about Robin Hood for hundreds of years. The stories first appeared in books around six hundred years ago. Some stories said Robin lived in the 1190s. He and his men were outlaws. An outlaw was "outside the law" and couldn't own a house or land. Anyone could kill an outlaw. At that time, there were many large forests in England, and outlaws often hid in the forests.

Was Robin Hood a real person? Nobody knows. Maybe the stories started with a real outlaw, but they changed and grew over the years. Robin Hood's bow and arrow became very important in the stories. From 1252, all English men between 15 and 60 years old had to have a bow and arrow and know how to use it. Could anyone shoot as well as Robin Hood? It's a good story. Even today, Robin Hood is one of the most famous and popular heroes in books, films and on TV, all around the world.

Activities

The answers are on page 40.

The contest begins

Choose the right word to finish each sentence.

1.

The day of the contest was
.... and sunny.

long   cold   bright

2.

The Sheriff got down from his
horse to .... the archers.

meet   watch   trick

3.

Some of the arrows didn't hit the
targets at all, and the crowd ....

cheered   laughed   helped

4.

"That's the best shooting
I've ever ...."

heard   seen   done

Mixed-up story

Can you put these pictures and sentences in order?

A.

The Sheriff got down from his horse to meet the archers.

B.

A boy was walking through the forest.

C.

Nobody saw the man in red again.

D.

The contest was in a wide field next to the castle.

E.

"You're a better archer even than Robin Hood."

F.

"I think the Sheriff needs another suprise."

G.

The man in red's arrow hit the Captain's arrow and split it in two.

H.

"The Sheriff is having an archery contest."

I.

One after another, the archers shot at the targets.

Who's who?

Choose *two* sentences for each person.

Robin Hood

The Sheriff

The Marshal

Little John

A.
He was angry with his soldiers.

B.
He wanted to bring the silver arrow to Sherwood.

C.
He told Robin the contest was a trick.

D.
He made his skin brown.

E.
He organized the Sheriff's contest.

F.
He asked the man in red to work for him.

G.
He was angry with the man in red.

H.
He knew how to send a message to the Sheriff.

The day of the contest

Which three things *can't* you see in the picture?

a town

someone
playing music

Robin Hood

a castle

archers

horses

the Sheriff

targets

someone
dancing

a silver
arrow

Say why...

Choose the right ending for each sentence.

1.

The Sheriff organised the contest because...

A. ...he really liked archery.

B. ...he wanted to catch Robin Hood.

2.

Robin Hood went to the contest because...

A. ...he wanted to rob the Sheriff.

B. ...he wanted to win the silver arrow.

3.

Robin Hood won the contest because...

A. ...his arrow split the Captain's arrow.

B. ...the Captain missed the target.

4.

The Marshal was angry because...

A. ...the man in red didn't want to work for the Sheriff.

B. ...the man in red ran away from the contest.

Word list

archer (n) a person who uses a bow and arrow. The sport or activity is called **archery** (n).

arrow (n) a thin piece of wood with a sharp point. Long ago, archers used bows and arrows in battles (for fighting), or to chase animals (hunting).

bow (n) a long piece of wood with a tight string. It is used to shoot arrows for fighting and hunting.

captain (n) the person in charge of a ship, or of a small group of soldiers.

cheer (v) when you cheer, you shout to show that you think something is really good and special.

contest (n) a competition to find the person who is the best at something.

edge (n) the furthest or outside part of something.

fireplace (n) the place in a room or house specially for burning fires.

foolish (adj) the opposite of clever or intelligent.

hall (n) the largest and most important room in a castle, or the first room in a house.

lady (n) a polite word for a woman, or the wife of an important man.

marshal (n) long ago, the person who organized a contest of fighting skills, such as archery or fighting on horseback. A marshal was usually a knight.

organize (v) when you organize something, you make sure that everything happens at the right time and everyone knows what to do.

persuade (v) if you don't want to do something, or you're not sure, someone might persuade you and then you will do it.

protect (v) to keep someone or something safe.

respect (v) if you respect someone or something, you think they are important or right, and you do what they say.

robbed (from **rob**, v) you are robbed when another person steals money or other valuable things from you.

servant (n) someone who works for another person, especially in their home.

sheriff (n) an important person who acts for the King, Queen or government in a part of the country.

shoot, shot (v) when you use a bow and arrow or a gun to hit something, you shoot.

split, split (v) when you split something, you separate it into two or more pieces.

step (v) when you move forward and start to walk, you step.

target (n) in a shooting contest, you use a target. Targets are often round. To win, you try to hit the middle of the target.

truth (n) something that is true.

Answers

The contest begins
1. bright
2. meet
3. laughed
4. seen

Mixed-up story
B, H, F, D, A,
I, G, E, C

Who's who?
Robin Hood – B, D
The Sheriff – A, F
The Marshal – E, G
Little John – C, H

The day of the contest
These things aren't in the picture:
a town, Robin Hood, a silver arrow.

Say why...
1. B
2. B
3. A
4. A

You can find information about
other Usborne English Readers here:
www.usborneenglishreaders.com

Designed by Hope Reynolds

Series designer: Laura Nelson Norris

Edited by Jane Chisholm

With thanks to Andy Prentice

Digital imaging: Nick Wakeford

Page 32: picture of book cover, from private collection
© Ken Walsh/Bridgeman images

First published in 2018 by Usborne Publishing Ltd.,
Usborne House, 83-85 Saffron Hill, London EC1N 8RT, England.
www.usborne.com Copyright © 2018 Usborne Publishing Ltd.